MW00892694

Nancy –
To my many wins!

Enjoy!

Russ Dore

ACKNOWLEDGEMENTS

I would like to thank my family members and friends who have read drafts of the book and offered their comments and suggestions, many of which I used in my revisions. In particular, I would like to thank my wife Judy who additionally helped in proofing the drafts for grammar, punctuation and clarity.

I would also like to acknowledge The Collections of the Henry Ford for permission to include the letter to Henry Ford included in Chapter 9.

PREFACE

This is a fictional account of the development of the Big Three automotive companies. Some of these meetings and conversations actually took place, however in most cases the events are strictly fictional and are based on the author's best judgement of what could have taken place. This judgement comes from years of research preparing for my live presentations on these automotive pioneers, which I have given to hundreds of groups. In other words, in my research I have gotten to know these individuals and their personalities. In fictional form, I have tried to flesh them out as real people. I hope you enjoy meeting them as much as I enjoyed putting words in their mouths!

I suggest that you refer to Appendix A from time to time to see visually where each individual fits in the drama as the Big Three developed. Appendix B provides brief biographies of the primary Big Three pioneers.

Russell Lee Doré, Ed.D.

April 1, 2021

CONTENTS

Chapter 1. Henry Ford Gets Things Rolling 1

Chapter 2. Laying the Groundwork for General Motors 5

Chapter 3. Billy Durant Founds General Motors 10

Chapter 4. Walter Chrysler Enters the Scene 18

Chapter 5. Billy's Road Back to Power...24

Chapter 6. The Dodge Brothers Make Trouble..31

Chapter 7. Billy Out at GM...34

Chapter 8. Walter Chrysler Gets His Own Company 36

Chapter 9. Changes at Ford...40

Chapter 10. Growth at GM 47

Chapter 11. Chrysler Becomes a Major Competitor 51

Chapter 12. The Workers Get a Voice in the Big Three....................................56

Chapter 13. The Arsenal of Democracy 60

Chapter 14. The Big Three Pioneers Exit the Scene 65

Appendix A. Individuals & Companies in the Formation of the Big Three 69

Appendix B. Brief Biographies of the Big Three Pioneers 71

About the Author..74

Chapter 1. Henry Ford Gets Things Rolling

In the spring of 1903 Alexander Malcomson greeted Henry Ford at the Malcomson Coal Company offices in Detroit.

"Henry, thanks for coming in today. I am speaking on behalf of a group of about a dozen investors which I pulled together. We're sorry that your last company, The Henry Ford Company, did not work out for you. At any rate, we're impressed with your racing success and we know you have a lot more name recognition now. Your 999 racer really is a winner, especially with Barney Oldfield driving it. We know you are also the best engineer in this new automobile industry. So we would like to set up another new company and call it the Ford Motor Company. You would be Vice President and Chief Engineer. What do you think?"

Henry looked puzzled. "Honestly, I am a bit surprised. As you know, my first company, the Detroit Automobile Company failed, and I was pushed out of my second company, the Henry Ford Company. So you still want me involved?"

"Yes, Henry, definitely. I believe in your ability, and as I said your name is a huge asset now because of the racing. I'm confident we can make it work this time."

"So I would get my name on the company, and some stock, I assume, along with a salary. Who would run the company?"

Malcomson replied quietly "John Gray, a banker, will be President. He will supply the financial knowledge we need to be a successful business."

Henry leaned back in his chair. "I don't know, Alex. I am 39 years old, and certainly don't want to be involved with another failure. But I sure love this business and want to succeed. You know the saying 'if you don't succeed at first, try, try again.' I fully agree with that. But there is another part that says, 'then quit before you make a fool of yourself.' So this would be my last try. Let me talk to Clara about this. My wife is always very supportive; in fact, I call her my 'great believer'. Let me talk it over with her and I'll get back with you." That evening after dinner he talked with Clara, and once again she believed! The Ford Motor Company was founded in June of 1903.

The next year Henry met with John and Horace Dodge, known for their red hair and earthy language. They were building almost all the mechanical components for Ford's first production car, the Model A, in their machine shop. Henry was assembling the components and adding the body, wheels, and tires at his first plant on Mack Avenue.

"Fellows, we have a bit of a problem," Henry started out. "We have a cash flow issue and will have to delay our payments to you for your last few shipments."

"Bull shit," exclaimed John loudly. "How in the Hell are we supposed to pay our workers and pay for our materials?"

" Easy, John, I am sure we can work something out. Our problem is we don't have the money until we make a few more sales, and so we need credit for a while."

"Credit? Henry, we are no damn bank. We are a machine shop. Tell you what, we might be able to squeeze by for a little while, but it will cost you. We will give you $10,000 credit in return for 20% of your company stock. That way it works for both of us."

John turned to his younger brother Horace, who was the more technical of the two. "That set with you, H.E.?", referring to him by his initials as he preferred, ever since being kidded about his name as a youth and being called "horse".

" Sounds good to me," Horace replied, turning to Henry. "We don't want your company to fold, because you are our biggest customer. On the other hand, there are a lot of small new automobile companies starting up and they're looking for suppliers like us. You are not the only show in town, you know."

"Fellows" commented Henry "I can take your proposal to our President John Gray. But I can tell you he will never go for 20%. I am willing to ask for 10% and may be able to sell that to him."

"All right, Henry, give that a try", said John. Henry talked to John Gray the next day, and the Dodge Brothers became 10% stockholders in Ford.

Ford built a new larger plant, the Piquette Plant. They starting building new models to replace the original Model A. They used the letters of the alphabet as model names, and so they had Model B, C, and so on. Some were large touring models, which the stockholders wanted because of the larger profit margins. But when they got to N, they had their first major commercial success, the small and practical Model N Runabout. Their supplier for the tires on this model was Harvey Firestone. Ford sold over 8,000 Model Ns and generated their first profit of over $1 million. Henry then envisioned a slightly larger car which he said would be a "car for the great multitude." By then they were up to the letter T.

Henry called one of his most trusted employees, Charlie Sorensen, to his office on the first floor of the Piquette Plant and closed the door. The handsome blonde Dane had the nickname "Cast Iron Charlie" due to his expertise in improving iron and steel casting methods.

"Charlie, I want to build an enclosed room on the third floor where we can develop the Model T. I don't want anyone but those of us working on it directly to see it. This car is going to make our future, and we need to protect it until it is ready to market. We are going to use a new steel alloy, vanadium, which will make it lighter, stronger and more flexible to survive the ruts in the roads. We also should look at a new way of manufacturing it. You know how we now build each car on a platform, and the workers bring the parts and their tools to the vehicle? Well, I'd like to try your idea of keeping the workers and their tools stationary and puling l the chassis past them as they add their parts. This moving assembly line could really reduce the costs of the Model T, and therefore reduce the price and make it available to everyone. It will be so low in price that no man making a good salary will be unable to own one."

Charlie stood up and commented" Sounds exciting, Henry. When do you want this room built?"

"Yesterday", replied Henry with a sly smile. "I want to get started on this project as soon as possible."

The Model T was launched in 1908. It was offered in 4 colors at a price of $850, and sales were through the roof, but delivery was way behind schedule. Concerned about the delay, Henry went out on the plant floor and asked what the problem was.

"Well, Mr. Ford, much of the holdup is with the colors. Some days we have too many green fenders and not enough red hoods. The next week it might be the other way around."

"I can solve that. Let's make them all black. Solves the problem of shortage of parts. Also, black paint is actually a little less expensive and dries a little faster so we win several ways with black paint. In fact, that can be a new motto for Ford. 'You can buy a car from us in any color you want, as long as it is black!"

Henry Ford had launched the first of what was to become one of the Big Three automotive companies, and he was finally on his way to becoming tremendously successful!

Chapter 2. Laying the Groundwork for General Motors

There were three automotive pioneers whose companies eventually became significant in forming General Motors that were all in operation before General Motors was founded.

The most significant was David Buick, a Scottish born engineer, who founded the Buick Manufacturing Company in Flint, Michigan in 1902 to develop automobiles. Buick built only 37 cars in 1904 and was in trouble. James Whiting of the Flint Wagon works invested heavily in Buick to save it from financial ruin. Another local wagon builder, Billy Durant, was a founder of the Durant-Dort Carriage Company which had become the country's largest builder of horse drawn carriages. Billy was known as "King of the Carriage Makers" and Flint was known as Vehicle City because it was the leading carriage-building city in the country. On a clear summer day in 1904, James Whiting invited Billy to lunch at his country club.

"Good to see you, Billy. As you know, I am a big promoter of the city of Flint. I'm looking ahead, and I think this new horseless carriage, the automobile, will eventually replace carriages. Then Flint will no longer be Vehicle City."

"Jim, do you really think these horseless carriages will stick? I think that they're just a fad."

"In my opinion they're not a fad. We do have a small start in automobile manufacturing here in town with David Buick's company. I was hoping we could add more automobile companies and then we would still be Vehicle City, but with automobiles rather than carriages. But there is one big problem."

"What's that?

"Buick is in trouble, so I just bought into it to try to save it. I think it can be successful with the right management."

"So who do you have in mind to manage it?"

"You, Billy. Anything you touch seems to turn to gold. You can turn this around."

"Me? I have no interest in automobiles. I have never even driven one. My daughter took a ride in one recently with a girlfriend, and I chewed her out for it. 'Risked your life in that contraption', I told her. So why don't you run Buick yourself?"

"I don't have the resources that you do. It's all I can do to run my own small carriage company. Look, automobiles are coming, and if Flint is to continue to be the leader in transportation manufacturing, we need a successful car company to get things started. And you are the only guy I know that can pull it off."

"You really think this is a big deal for the future of our city, don't you?"

"Yes, I definitely do. Look, do me a favor. A friend of mine has a Buick Model 20 that he will loan us. Drive it for a couple of months and see what you think. I bet you will see the light. Do it as a favor for an old friend and for your city!"

"Well, you really put me on the spot, Jim. OK, just for you I'll take you up on the deal. But don't get your hopes up. I will be honest with you after I try this thing out."

After driving the Buick over all kinds of roads Durant saw the light and got a glimpse of the future. He took over management of Buick and eventually bought a third interest in the company. Under Billy's leadership, by 1908 it was the number one automobile company in sales.

The Olds Motor Works was another early company which eventually played a key role in the formation of GM. Founded in 1899 by automotive pioneer Ransom E. Olds, it became the largest car company in the country. In 1905 Olds entered the office of his chief financial backer, Fred Smith, at their plant in Lansing, Michigan. "Fred, we need to talk. I am tired of you meddling in the production operations. The last straw is that

I just found out you have set up an experimental engineering shop without my knowledge."

Smith replied, with some embarrassment, "You know I told you a while back that I wanted to have a quality certification program and needed this shop to do it. You kept putting me off, so I just went ahead. This new certification could be a great marketing advantage for us."

"That idea is not worth the cost of implementing it, as I told you before. But there is a bigger issue. My name is on the plant here in Lansing. It says 'Olds Motor Works' if you haven't noticed. So I should be able to decide how we are going to handle things. Our Curved Dash Oldsmobile is the best-selling vehicle in the country by far. I don't want to mess with success."

"Ransom, I am responsible to the stockholders and on some issues, I need to call the shots."

"Well then, you can call them by yourself. I've been thinking about this for a while, and with our many differences, it's time for me to leave."

"Probably a good move. You realize the Oldsmobile name stays with us."

"Yes," Ransom agreed. "A contract is a contract, and I am not going to fight it."

Later that year Ransom E. Olds formed REO Motors, using his initials in the name. By 1908 REO was outselling Oldsmobile, and Oldsmobile was in financial trouble.

A Vermont native, Henry Leland, also contributed significantly to development of GM. He opened the Leland & Falkner Machine shop in Detroit which made engines for the Curved Dash Oldsmobile. One day in 1902 he met with Nicholas Herrick, manufacturing manager at Olds, in Herrick's small office off the shop floor.

"Nick, this new 10 horsepower engine can be a fine engine for the Curved Dash Olds. More power, which is what people are looking for these days."

"It sounds great, but just one problem."

"What's that?"

"I am concerned about the chassis being able to handle the increased weight and power."

"You're right. You can beef up the chassis and suspension a bit to handle that, though."

"Sounds easy, Henry, but that takes new tooling fixtures and adds to the materials costs."

"But it will pay off in customer acceptance and you can recover the costs by a small price increase."

Herrick frowned." You know, this Curved Dash model is selling like mad. We are the largest mass producer of cars in the country. If we made these changes, we could not keep up with production to meet our sales orders. I think we will table this new engine until we develop a new model that can handle it."

"I think that's a big mistake, "said Henry as he stood to leave.

"That's our decision, Henry."

Leland was asked by another company to help them with a project later that year. William Murphy was running the Henry Ford Company, Henry Ford's second company. They had just let Henry Ford go because they felt he was not developing new models fast enough. Leland sat down across the large mahogany desk from Murphy, who opened the conversation. "As we told you earlier, we are folding up this Henry Ford Company. We hired you to appraise the equipment so that we can liquidate it. Do you have your figures for me today?"

"Yes, Bill, but before we go over them, let me tell you my idea. You have a pretty good operation here, and I think it can be saved. I have the engineering background to help you do this. I also have a new 10 horsepower engine I developed for Olds, but they're not interested now. If we put this new engine in the body you already have, I think it can be a winner."

"You really think so? We certainly would like to make a go of it rather than shut it down. Of course we would have to change the name. You can't have a Henry Ford Company with no Henry Ford," Murphy chuckled.

"You know, I have been thinking about possibly starting my own company, and would call it Cadillac, after the French explorer who settled Detroit. What do you think of that name?"

"Actually, I kind of like it. Ties nicely in with the history of the city."

"How about it?" said Leland smiling. "Can we give this a go?"

"I think we might have a deal. Let me talk it over with my partners and I'll get back to you."

Cadillac was founded later that year and achieved a reputation for excellence. In 1908 it was awarded the prestigious Dewar Trophy by the Royal Automobile Club of London. Henry Leland did not realize that he had saved a small company that would someday be part of the world's largest corporation, General Motors.

Chapter 3. Billy Durant Founds General Motors

It was a big day for Billy Durant and his Buick Motors Company in the summer of 1908. He was launching a bold new venture as he greeted his guests Henry Ford, Ransom Olds and Ben Briscoe at the door to his hotel suite at the Pontchartrain Hotel in Detroit. "Good afternoon, Henry. How are you, Ransom? Good to see you, Ben. Have you both met Ben Briscoe, of Maxwell-Briscoe? Thank you all for coming today. Sorry we had to move the meeting to my room here at the hotel, but I was afraid the press would make a big deal about us getting together since they had learned about our scheduled meeting at the Penobscot Building. Don't get me wrong, it is a big deal, but we don't need to work on it in public." Durant motioned for them to sit down at the table and he offered them coffee and tea.

"I will get right to the point. I think we can put together the world's best car company by combining our companies and our talents. Henry, you have a nice little company, and your Model N Runabout is selling well. Your new Model T looks even better. Ransom, you built Oldsmobile into a fine company and now you are building REO Motors. I am sure REO will be an even better company than Oldsmobile, now that you don't have to fight with your investors and are free to do things your way. Ben, your Maxwell brand is doing very well, as we all know. And there is my company, Buick Motors."

Ben interjected "Don't be so humble, Billy. Buick Motors is first in sales for the whole industry, which is over 400 companies."

Billy smiled. "Thanks, Ben. I know this merger was your idea, and the JP Morgan people talked to you about it. They put together several companies to form US Steel, which worked out pretty well for all concerned and they think we should do the same with automotive companies. I know they suggested to you that we include the top 20 companies. Maybe I am not a big enough thinker, but I felt we should keep it simple and start with the four of us. A lot better chance of putting together a deal.

Henry spoke up. "I think you are right. I like more straightforward and simple approaches myself. What about you other two fellows?'

Ransom nodded his head. "Sounds good to me. I think we have a good crew here to do this."

Ben chimed in "I guess I have to agree with you fellows. We probably could add others later if we felt it made sense at that time. I'm in."

Henry turned toward Billy. "Let's talk about the money. I talked with my young business manager Jimmy Couzens and he feels that we would need about three million in cash, plus of course stock in the company."

Billy replied "Wow, I didn't think there would be a need for so much cash to get started. We all will get stock in what will grow into the world's largest car company. There should be plenty of payback down the line."

Henry stood up, walked toward the window, then turned back toward the group. "You have to realize that Ford Motor Company is finally showing nice profits, and our stockholders, all 12 of us, have waited a while for that, and feel that we need whoever finances this new operation to provide some incentive for us giving up our independence. We feel we have a good future now. Maybe we will never be one of the world's biggest companies, but this deal has to give us a better future than we would have on our own. Besides, I kind of like having my name on the building, and not having to answer to anyone but my present stockholders, and even then sometimes they can be a pain in the behind!"

Ransom had been sitting quietly listening to Henry. "You know, I was going to come in for stock only, but you make a good point, Henry. I agree with your thinking, so I will also need some cash. This is a big move for all of us, and we need to feel it is well worth it."

Billy seemed taken aback. "Well, fellows, this comes as a bit of a shock. I thought we had a once-in-a-lifetime opportunity here to all be a part of something really big. I know we are all self-made successes, not a bunch of Ivy-League boys who have always had big bucks. Here is a chance to out-do the Ivy-leaguers. To be brutely honest, I think it is somewhat short-sighted to worry about cash up-front. But I hear you, and we are all businessmen, and we know business is about negotiation and compromise. So let Ben and I go back to the other investors and see what we can come up with. OK?"

Henry said, "Fine with me."

Ransom added "Yes, just keep us posted."

The next week Billy called Ben. "I guess this is not going through. My other investors are not keen on coming up with cash, and as an investor I feel the same. There is a great future here, and that should be enough incentive to come aboard. Maybe we can look at a couple of other companies to bring in. What do you think?"

 "I think we will just run into the same situation. Automobile company founders are a pretty independent lot. Pretty hands-on, and not necessarily long -term thinkers like you. I think I will pass on this deal, too. I may regret it, but it looks like too much of a struggle to put it together, and I need to devote my energies to running my own company. It was a good try, Billy. You were the biggest guy in the carriage business before you got into this crazy car business, so maybe you can pull it off. Good luck to you."

Billy was disappointed, but being the eternal optimist, he took a night train to Lansing to try another approach. Since Ransom Olds had left Oldsmobile and formed REO Motors, Oldsmobile had been run by Fred Smith and Billy knew it was losing money. At 3am he arrived at the plant, and Fred Smith gave him a tour. "You seem to have a pretty good operation here, Fred. I think I can help you turn it into a profitable operation. Here is my idea. I want to put together several automobile companies into a major corporation. We can be the biggest and best in the world. I have Buick, and I would like to add Oldsmobile. I was thinking of the name Universal Motors for the corporate name, but somebody already has a claim on that. So I think I will call it General Motors. What do you think?"

"Sounds appropriate to me. As a financial guy, I need to know the terms."

Billy answered, "Your stockholders will get stock in the new corporation in exchange for your Oldsmobile shares."

"What, no cash for us? "

"Hell no, Fred. You are losing your ass here. You get stock and a tremendous opportunity to make money in the future. Big money!"

"I will take it to my investors, Billy. Personally, I want to get back in the black and this might be the best way for us. What we are doing now is certainly not working, and you have done a great job at Buick since taking over. You are known as the master salesman in the industry, and I trust that you can bring us into profitability. I think I can convince the rest of the stockholders to make this deal with you. Let me give it a try."

Fred Smith was successful in selling the deal to his investors. General Motors was incorporated on September 16, 1908 and announced to the press in December. General Motors consisted of Buick and Oldsmobile, and Billy's dream was now launched.

Billy ran into Henry Ford at the Detroit Auto Show in 1909. "How's the new company going, Billy?"

Billy shook his hand and said "Good, Henry, Good. You know that I bought your old Henry Ford Company from Henry Leland. Of course, it is now Cadillac, which Leland renamed it after you left, as you know. They should never have pushed you out. I never could figure out what those investors were thinking. Anyway, there is still room for your present Ford Motor Company in General Motors. I'm not going to give up on convincing you to join us."

Henry replied" Thanks, but my Ford Motor Company means a lot to me. My first company, the Detroit Automobile Company didn't work out, and neither did the Henry Ford Company as you said. So this was my third and last try. If it didn't work out, I was going to see if I could go back to working at the Edison Illuminating plant. But it looks like I won't be doing that. You see, this new Model T of ours is selling like hot cakes. It is not as fancy as your Buicks or Oldsmobiles, but the common man is buying them like crazy."

"Henry, I have wanted to add a smaller, less costly car to our line-up at General Motors, but my Board is more interested in the larger, pricier cars. Bigger profit margin. But as you are showing people, with higher volume on the cheaper cars you end up with more profits in the long run. Maybe someday I can convince them. But by then it might be too late. You're grabbing most of that market share, and there may not be enough market left for us."

Henry grinned "Well, as you know I like to keep things simple and this simple low-cost car appeals to the masses."

Later that year, in October, Billy learned that Henry and James Couzens were in New York, staying at the Belmont Hotel, near Billy's New York office. He asked to see them, and they agreed. Henry was suffering from lumbago, so Billy and Couzens met in the lobby of the hotel while Henry stretched out on his bed in his room. Billy said "I know you are busy and are here on business, so I will get right to the point. I want to make one more try at bringing Ford into General Motors. I will offer Henry eight million dollars for Ford. That's a hell of a deal, Jimmy."

Couzens replied "It is at that and I'm in favor of it. Mr. Ford and I have been working awfully hard, and neither one of us is in the greatest of health. It would be great to walk away and let someone grow the company and deal with all the problems. Let me go up and talk with him."

14

Couzens came back to the lobby." Mr. Ford likes your deal of $8 million. We need $6 million in cash, with $2 million of it up front. Then $4 million of it can be paid out over three years at 5 percent interest. The remaining $2 million would be in stock in General Motors."

"I think we can do that, Jimmy. I am really excited about bringing Ford into our new corporation. That stock will be worth a lot in few years. I hope Henry is giving you some shares."

"Yes, he is" shrugged Jimmy without much enthusiasm.

"Jimmy, you are a pretty good negotiator for a young fellow. I hope you are negotiating well for yourself this time. Anyway, I will get our deal approved by my board and get back to you right away."

Two weeks later the usually upbeat Billy called Jimmy. He sounded solemn "I'm sorry, Jimmy, I couldn't raise the two million up-front cash. My bank, National City Bank, said I have been buying too many companies lately and they feel I am overextended credit-wise. They also made a comment that this little Ford company is no big deal, so I needed to pass on it. I certainly disagree with that. These bankers don't have the same confidence in the future of the automobile industry as we do. I know Henry doesn't like bankers. But they have been pretty good to me in the past with loans, but right now I am not feeling so good about them. I know you said that Henry was firm on the two million cash up front, so I am not going to push it any further. Good luck to you and Henry, and I know you will grow your company. I am sure we'll be major competitors for years. I wish it would be as partners instead, but I guess it was not meant to be. Give my regards to Henry." So for the second and final time, Billy's attempt to add Ford to General Motors was dead. Billy thought to himself how close he had come, and how different the industry would have looked if he had succeeded!

Billy quickly added another existing automobile company which would become a major division of GM. Edward Murphy, not to be confused with

William Murphy of Cadillac, in1907 had founded the Oakland Motor Car Company in Pontiac, Michigan, which was named after Oakland County, where Pontiac is located. In February of 1909 Billy Durant visited Murphy at his office in Pontiac. "Hello, Ed, nice little company you have here. You have a fine product in the low-price range."

"Thanks, Billy. Al Brush is our engineer. I am just the money man. Al deserves the credit for the car's success."

"Let me come to the point of my visit. I understand Oakland has some financial issues. I'm always looking for companies to add to GM. Any interest in selling?"

"I don't think so, Billy. We have only been at it about a year, and we are finally picking up steam. Our only issue with growth is financing. We can't grow until we have more capital, and you know how the banks view the automobile business. They're not willing to loan us anything."

"Maybe we can work something out. How about if we buy a 49% interest in Oakland? Would that help?"

"Of course. But GM would be competing with itself. Seems strange to me."

"Yes, Ed, it seems a little strange, but it would give us a financial interest in another vehicle and would be better for us than starting a new car line from scratch."

"I could see this as a possible win for both of us," commented Murphy as he leaned back thoughtfully. "Let me take it to my Board."

GM purchased a 49% interest in Oakland, and later that year when Edward Murphy unfortunately passed away, GM acquired full interest. After they introduced the Pontiac, a slightly higher priced model which outsold the Oakland model, the name of the division was changed to Pontiac. Pontiac, along with Buick, Oldsmobile, and Cadillac, became a major division of GM. In 1911 he added a truck division, General Motors

Company (GMC) by combining the Rapid Motor Vehicle Company of Pontiac and the Reliance Truck Company of Lansing.

Chapter 4. Walter Chrysler Enters the Scene

Charlie Nash welcomed Walter Chrysler to his Buick Division President's office. "How are you, young man? Did you have a good trip from Pittsburg?"

"Yes," replied Walter," it's a pleasure to meet you. Buick is quite an operation, and I am flattered to be asked here to talk to you about a job."

Charlie continued." Our President here at General Motors, Jim Storrow, who is also on the Board of your company, American Locomotive, told us about you. He said you are one of the best manufacturing talents around. He also told us the story of how you bought a Locomobile automobile 3 years ago at the Chicago Auto Show for $5000, mostly borrowed. Then, as I understand it, you didn't drive it for 3 months, but took it apart to study it and then put it back together. I love someone with that curiosity and interest in automobiles."

Walter smiled faintly. "What he didn't tell you was that my wife was not pleased about me buying that car, not pleased at all. She didn't scold me, but it did seem that when she closed the kitchen door it made a little more noise than usual; maybe she slammed it!"

Charlie laughed." I guess I am not too surprised at that!"

Walter got more animated as he went on. "I was fascinated by this new means of transportation. I would like to get in on the ground floor in this new industry. I don't have a lot of fancy formal education, so I may be about as far as I can go in the Locomotive business. Besides, it's an old industry, and I see more opportunity for me in automobiles."

"Well, Walter, I think we have a good fit for you. We would like to offer you the Works Manager position here at Buick, at a salary of $6000 a year. We understand that matches your salary at American Locomotive. We feel that's a good offer, considering you have no automobile experience. Except, of course, rebuilding your Locomobile car", he added with a smile.

Walter chuckled "Yes, that is true. What I bring you is my manufacturing experience as Works Manager at the locomotive company. I guess you've heard that I am organized, cost-conscious and good with people, or I wouldn't be here. It sounds like a fair deal for both parties. We are both betting on the future: you are betting that I will quickly learn automobile manufacturing and I am betting that I will have a higher salary eventually."

"You seem like a quick study, Walter, and you summed it up perfectly. Shall we shake on the deal?"

"Sure," smiled Walter, "I think we both got a good deal."

Walter went back to his company and handed in his resignation. His Vice-President, Greg Moore asked, "What are they paying you?"

"Six thousand a year, same as I make here."

"No raise? Tell you what, Walter, we were about ready to give you a raise. What would it take to keep you here?"

"More than you would want to pay" replied Walter.

Greg came back "Walter, you are a key to our manufacturing productivity and profitability. How about if we double your salary to twelve thousand a year? How's that for recognition of your value to us?"

Walter paused, and then spoke quietly "I'm honored, truly. I have given this a lot of thought. I can see a real future in this new automobile industry, especially if I can get in early and work my way up. I am confident I can go a long way. My father was a locomotive engineer, and I followed him into the locomotive business and have really enjoyed it. But I have kind of peaked here at American Locomotive. I don't have the formal education to move up to your job. The automotive guys are mostly self-made and hands-on, like me. Besides, these new automobiles are fun! They are smaller than locomotives and offer more opportunities to be creative. I have more of an eye for design and appearance than most of those guys and have some ideas on how to make the products even more attractive to the buyers. Bottom line, Greg, I have made up my mind to go."

"Well, we made you a great offer. You have always been a confident guy, sometimes overconfident, but you have pulled it off every time. Personally, I think you may pull it off again in the auto industry. All I can say is best of luck. I won't be completely surprised if someday I see an ad for a Chrysler automobile."

Walter smiled "I won't either, Greg."

Walter showed up in Flint in 1911 at Buick and in his first week he found out that three or four cars per week were taken out of the plant for a test drive and never returned. He set up a registration system to prevent the theft by employees and saved the company much of his first year's salary. He also used his previous manufacturing experience to greatly improve the operations and profitability of Buick.

In the fall of 1912, Charlie Nash called Walter in to his office, shut the door and motioned for him to sit down. He said " I want you to know that you have been doing a wonderful job for us in the short time you have been with us and we really appreciate it. I've asked you to come here today so I can tell you about some important changes coming about at GM that will affect us all."

Walter felt his body tightening up a bit. This sounded a lot like the opening he used when he had to lay someone off or demote them due to economic or organizational changes.

Charlie continued," As you know, back in 1910 before you got here, the recession hurt our bottom line at GM. Our large models were not selling. Henry Ford's Model T was doing much better. We had to borrow a lot of money to keep afloat. A syndicate of twenty-two banks was formed to manage it. They set up a five-man directorate to do this. Unfortunately, Billy Durant had to step down as President of GM. He is now one of the five directors but has only one vote like the rest. One of the bankers, James Storrow, became President. Those changes worked out well. Now the company is making some changes again."

Walter's heart beat a little faster. Were they eliminating his position, and letting him go? How could he survive? He had not been there that long. Or were they putting in someone above him that would block his possibilities for a promotion? Probably some guy with a college degree. Maybe he should have stayed at the locomotive company where he had a lot of security. Maybe this new automobile industry was too volatile.

Charlie leaned forward, resting one hand on his desk. "Our President James Storrow has done a good job of turning us around, but he is a banker, not a car guy. They now want a car guy in charge, and are promoting me to President of GM."

Here it comes, thought Walter! They are bringing in some new guy to head Buick, and he is bringing in his own Works Manager to replace me. Charlie smiled and said "Walter, we are promoting you to President of Buick." The words did not seem real. Walter just sat there. "I said we are promoting you to President of Buick. I have never seen you at a loss for words. Are you all right?"

"Yes, yes, I'm all right." Walter leaned back in his chair. "It just took a minute to set in. I never told you this, but I had started planning on this possibility in my mind about 6 months ago when I saw clearly that I could do the job."

"I have always said, Walter, that you never lacked for confidence, nor humility, at times. But I like that. I will take a man who is good and knows it every time over a man who is not good but thinks he is." He reached out and shook Walter's hand.

"You will not be disappointed, believe me. With you in the head shed and me running Buick Division, Henry Ford better look out. If he looks in his rear-view mirror, he will see us right on his ass and gaining fast."

Not long after Walter took over Buick his personable and down-to-earth nature became evident. One day at lunchtime after a meeting one of his executives suggested that they go over to the Book Cadillac Hotel for lunch. "No, today let's eat here in the employee cafeteria." He led them into the room filled with assembly line workers in their dirty overalls. He walked over to a table where 5 men were seated and said "Hello, boys. I'm Walter Chrysler. Mind if I sit down? "

"No, please sit down" one of the workers answered.

"Boys, do you have any ideas on how to improve your jobs? How can we help you be even more productive? Let's hear your thoughts." After a brief hesitation, the workers shared their ideas.

After 3 years at Buick, Walter had a great track record. One afternoon he asked for a meeting with Charlie to discuss his future. "Charlie, I came here for no increase from my previous salary at American Locomotive because I was betting on the future. The future is here. I got a nice raise when I was promoted to President of Buick, in fact you doubled my salary to $12,00 and gave me a bonus each year. But I feel I should be compensated more for my contribution to profits."

"What did you have in mind, Walter?"

"I was thinking of $50,000 a year."

"Fifty thousand? Holy shit, that is a big step from your base of $12,000."

Walter held up his hand as Charlie was about to continue. "I know, but I have a better idea of what other companies pay for manufacturing people like me. Good people, not average people. There are some good opportunities out there in the industry."

Charlie nodded," You're right. We were about ready to do something more for you, but $50,000 is out of the question."

"You know, I really want to stay here but I need to grow before all the best jobs are gone. I will consider $25,000 next year and $50,000 starting the year after that. If not, I think I will start looking."

"Walter, I hear you and knowing you and your confidence in yourself, I know you are not just blowing smoke. I will take your request to the board, with my personal recommendation. I can't promise anything, but I sure don't want to lose you."

"Thanks, Charlie, I appreciate your support."

A few days later Charlie stopped by Walter's office at Buick. With a smile on his face, he told Walter that the Board had approved the raise and the agreement for more in the future. Walter felt his already high self-confidence jump up a big notch! He felt that he might have found a home for the rest of his career.

Chapter 5. Billy's Road Back to Power

Louis Chevrolet and his brother Arthur were race car drivers who were born in Switzerland and grew up in France. Billy had met them back when he was still President of GM. They had approached Billy then and asked to join his Buick race team. He said, "Let's see you fellows race. I'll set up a race between you two and see how you do." After the race he looked at Louis, with his oversized mustache, and said with a chuckle, "Louie, you are very good, even though you are a bit wild. You can join the race team."

He turned to Arthur. "You're a good driver but a bit too cautious, I feel. Would you consider being my chauffer?" They both agreed.

Buick won half of all races in the US in the next couple of years. Louis then left the Buick team to be a free agent in 1909.

Louie contacted Billy again in 1911 and set up a meeting with him at a local restaurant. At this time Billy was serving as one of the five directors of General Motors, having been removed as President. Louis opened the conversation. "Billy, I want to start a car company. My name has a lot of recognition because of my racing success. I don't know much about business, so that's why I am talking to you. Maybe we could work together again. What do you think?"

"You hit me at a good time. I'm kind of bored being just a director at GM. I have always thought that GM should build a smaller, less expensive car to compete with Henry Ford. Look at the success he has had with the Model N. But my Board always turned me down. They like the profit margins on the big models. So let's talk more." And talk they did. Billy incorporated Chevrolet Motor Company in 1911 while still a director at GM. Louis got 100 shares of stock in the new company, but no cash. Their first plant was in Detroit, and Billy and his family moved there in 1912.

That same year they launched their first two models. "Louie, I am convinced our new company will be a success. Look at the advantages of our Chevrolet over Ford. A self-starter instead of a crank, and electric lights. A three-speed clutch transmission instead of Ford's two pedal planetary design.

Louie smiled broadly beneath his huge mustache. "I'm proud to have my name on the car. It will really appeal to the public and draw a lot of potential Ford buyers. It costs a little more, but it looks so far like people are willing to pay for the extra features."

GM had purchased the AC Spark Plug Company back while Billy was President. Seeing the value of owning parts suppliers, early in 1916 Billy formed his own supplier company, United Motors, by putting together a collection of 5 parts manufacturers. Billy felt that 41-year-old Alfred Sloan, the President of one of the companies, Hyatt Roller Bearings, was an exceptional talent. Right after he had finalized the purchase of the 5 companies, he called Sloan into his office.

"Al, you have done a fine job running Hyatt."

"Thanks," Al replied with a smile. "I'm excited about being a part of this new United Motors that you are putting together."

"That's what I wanted to talk to you about this morning, Al. I want you to leave Hyatt....."

"What?" Al quickly interrupted." You just complemented me and now you are going to sack me?"

"Let me finish. I want you to leave Hyatt to become President of the new company United Motors. You will be leading all 5 divisions, not just Hyatt!"

"Billy, that shook me up for a moment. I shouldn't have interrupted you."

"Al, you have the leadership ability to run the new company. Also, it's about time I get some more people like you on board who have more formal education. Your engineering degree from MIT is very impressive."

"Thanks, I did learn a lot there that has been very helpful in building Hyatt."

Billy leaned forward. "It isn't just the degree that impressed me about you. When I checked you out, I found that you had street smarts as well as book smarts."

"I've learned a lot from running a company that wasn't in the books."

"Well, you will need both kinds of smarts running United. We'll be a major parts supplier to much of the auto industry. I assume you are accepting.

"With pleasure," replied Al with a broad smile. "With great pleasure."

In the spring of 1916 Billy stopped by the Chevrolet plant to talk with Louie Chevrolet. "Louie, I want to fill you in on my latest plan. I plan to take over GM."

"Really, Billy? You are a real dreamer, but this sounds like a pipedream. Take over GM? You and what army?"

"No army needed, just paper. We'll offer to trade 5 shares of Chevrolet stock for every share of GM stock. At some point, if things go as I think, Chevrolet will hold a majority of shares of GM stock and we can take over. I wanted to tell you this today, before tomorrow's Chevrolet Board meeting where I will ask for approval of this plan. As a Chevrolet stockholder, I want your vote. What do you think?"

Louis stood up. "I think you are crazy, Billy. Crazy like a fox. Let's go for it!"

The Chevrolet Board approved the stock offer and they started offering their stock to GM stockholders. And the GM stockholders went for it big-time. Chevrolet piled up volumes of GM stock. At a GM Board meeting in 1916, Billy got up and announced that Chevrolet now had controlling interest in GM. Pierre DuPont, who made his fortune in making explosives like TNT, was now a major stockholder in GM. He took the position that GM should roll Chevrolet into GM, keeping GM as the corporate entity. In return for this, he proposed that Billy once again be elected President of GM. This was accomplished in June of that year, and Billy was back at the helm!

With Billy back as President, there was no job for Charlie Nash, so he took over the Thomas Jeffery automobile company in Kenosha, Wisconsin and named it Nash Motors. He offered Walter Chrysler a very nice position with him and Walter handed in his resignation to GM. Billy, who was now living in New York, took a night train to Flint and showed up in Walter's office at Buick first thing in the morning.

"Walter, what is this about resigning? I understand Charlie Nash has made you a nice offer to join him. How good an offer?"

" I would rather not say. But very generous or I wouldn't leave."

" Fair enough. That's your personal business, I know. I did a lot of thinking on the train last night, and I am prepared to offer you $500,000 a year to stay. You would need to commit to a 3-year contract, at minimum. How does that sound?" Walter sat there silently. "Walter, what do you have to say?"

"Yes, yes of course. I just was letting it soak in. That is too good an offer to refuse. And I am assuming the stock options that I have now will continue. Just one condition, Billy, and that is that you let me run Buick without you going to anyone under me. You know you have a tendency to do that, from the old days when you were just starting the company. But if you pay me that much to run Buick, let me run it. All I ask is that you go through me with any decisions."

"I will try. You know that they say that you can't teach an old dog new tricks, and I'm an old dog now. Just kidding, of course. You are right about asking for that, and I will commit to doing it. So do we have a deal?"

"Of course, Billy. I look forward to continuing to build Buick. And now that GM has the Chevrolet brand, I think we can kick Henry Ford's ass in the market. Let's do it. Let's get to work on it".

At the New York Auto show later in the fall, Billy had a drink with Henry Ford." What can I order for you, Henry? A bourbon or a brandy?"

" Just a lemonade, thanks."

"That's right, I forgot you aren't a drinker. Good to see you again. Now that I am living in New York, I don't see you Detroit fellows as much anymore. Your Model T is really doing well. You know, the success of that car inspired me to develop the Chevrolet for that same market."

Henry took a sip of his lemonade and then commented, "And you are doing very well with it. And I am quite impressed with how you got back the Presidency of GM. I guess we are the two big dogs in the fight, now. And the American people are the winners in this fight. I always wanted a car for the common man, which I gave them, and now they have two. Do you realize that we are changing American society? People can travel to where the work is, and to see family and to vacation. We have finally replaced the horse and buggy for good."

"And made a good buck in doing it, I must say," Billy added with a big grin.

"Billy, I understand that you folks are building a huge new headquarters building on West Grand Boulevard in Detroit. That takes a lot of bucks. And they are calling it the Durant Building. Even putting your initial D in each top corner."

 "Yes, that is the Board's idea. Some of us wonder if it isn't too big. They feel we will grow into it eventually. And they say that I am the dreamer! Well, I have a dinner to get to with some suppliers, so I better get along. Good to see you again. I never have quite gotten over the fact that we could not get you into GM, but it looks like it worked out even better for you by going your own way. Best of luck to you. I feel that having a good competitor makes us both stronger."

"I guess that is true. Just don't get too strong. I kind of like being number one!"

Meanwhile, Walter Chrysler was developing his managerial skills running Buick. His main frustration, however, was Billy Durant. He would approve a decision of Walter's and then Walter would learn that Billy had gone ahead on his own and in a different direction, undercutting Walter's authority. When Walter confronted him with it, he always apologized but justified it as making sense. In 1919 came the final straw. Walter was negotiating with the A.O. Smith company in Milwaukee to build Buick frames there. He went to a Flint Chamber of Commerce meeting and the President of the Chamber proudly announced that he had just received a wire from Billy Durant that they were building a new $6 million plant in Flint to manufacture Buick frames. He was excited at the jobs this would bring to Flint. After the meeting, Walter went to see Billy.

As Walter entered Billy's office, his irritation was clearly evident. "What's this about the announcement of the new frame plant in Flint? You know I am negotiating a contract with A.O. Smith to build them in Milwaukee. We are just about ready to sign the deal."

"I know, Walter, but I got thinking that we should have those jobs in Flint. This is where Buick started, and I feel we should support the town where we started and where our Buick headquarters is."

"Damn it, Billy, it just doesn't make sense. It would take 2 years to build the plant, and we need the additional frames now. Also, we have already added so many new jobs so quickly in Flint that there is no housing for the additional employees needed. Workers are already living in tent cities outside town, waiting for housing to be built for them." As he went on his voice rose. "I don't know what in the hell you were thinking. And from a finance standpoint, we will save a million and a half dollars a year buying the frames from A.O. Smith. We had this all figured out. Give me some credit."

Billy replied," Cool down, Walter. I know I should have talked to you about my idea, but I just came up with it. I have talked to a couple of Board members about it and they are supportive. I am bringing it up tomorrow at the GM Board meeting. Let's see how it goes tomorrow and how the Board feels."

"Fine, I will be at the Board meeting and will tell them just what I told you, and I won't sugar coat my objections. You want me to run Buick profitably, I damn well will run Buick profitably", Walter said as he abruptly rose and left the office.

Billy brought up the new plant at the Board meeting, and Walter was adamant about his objections and strongly presented his reasons. The plant was never built in Flint, and the frames were purchased from A.O. Smith. Walter knew this strong opposition would not set well with Billy, but at this point he didn't care. His 3 years were about up, and he left GM shortly. He sold his stock in GM for $10 million. He was 44 years old, rich and without a job.

Chapter 6. The Dodge Brothers Make Trouble

Henry Ford was making a lot of money on his Model T. He was the first to use a moving assembly line to reduce the production costs and thereby reduce his selling price to capture a big share of the market. He was investing profits in the huge new Rouge plant he was planning. Some of his stockholders, particularly the Dodge Brothers, disagreed and wanted higher dividends paid out now. John and Horace Dodge met with Henry at his Highland Park plant in 1918 to discuss this issue.

John Dodge, the older brother, took the lead, speaking forcefully "We're concerned about the dividends you are paying to stockholders. We know you're raking in the profits and feel we should be sharing more in the success. We want to grow our own business, too, and should have the money we deserve. Why should you hold out on us?"

"Take it easy, John. Let me explain. We are investing in the huge new Rouge plant we need for the future. The Highland Park plant is too small and outdated already. Once the Rouge plant is operating, we'll increase our dividends and we'll all have plenty of money. But we need the cash now to build the new plant."

John retorted, "Hell, we need money for our plants too, but we need it now. We know you'll make more parts in-house once the Rouge plant is finished. That will cut down on the parts we supply you now, and so we need to ramp up for new customers. You may have it all your way in your company, but we stockholders have a legal right to fair dividends. And we are damn well going to get them."

"Cool down, John. We've worked together for years and I have always treated you fairly."

"And it worked the other way too" chimed in Horace with a faint smile. "We made more components in your first couple models than you did. All you did was assemble our parts, put your name on the finished cars and sell them. Your reputation for quality was because we made you quality parts. You deserved the profits from those cars because you put the operation together and took the risks of buying the parts. But now we are stockholders, sharing the risks, and we want to share the profits. Now, Henry, not later. We may have started out as just mechanics, but we've learned a thing or two about business. So don't try to bull-shit us."

Henry sat there silent for a minute. "Well, I'm sorry you fellows can't see the long-run picture. But even though you are significant stockholders, there are many other stockholders and they are willing to wait. We need that money for the Rouge plant and we're going to stick to our plan."

"All right," boomed John as he stood up. "If you want to play hard-ball, so can we. As we said, we have a legal right to more dividends, so see you in court. And we damn well plan to win. "Horace rose and the brothers walked out. They gained the support of the other stockholders and took Ford to court. The court ruled in favor of the stockholders and ordered dividends of over $19 million be paid to them. That gave the Dodges about $2 million in cash right away.

Henry was furious, and he and Edsel bought out the remaining stockholders two years later. In the buyout, the Dodges received another $25 million. Not bad for their initial investment about 10 years earlier of $10,000! They gave Ford notice that they would no longer build components for Ford. They already had started a small Dodge Brothers auto company of their own back in 1914 and now had the money to take it big. Just as with Cadillac, Henry indirectly contributed to the development of this major competitor. In 1920, the Ford Motor Company was reorganized with all shares held by Henry, his son Edsel and other family members. He said rather than ever have outside stockholders again, he would tear down each one of his plants brick by brick. As part of the buyout, James Couzens sold his shares to Henry Ford for $30 million, and went on to serve as Mayor of Detroit and US Senator from Michigan.

The Dodge Brothers built both automobiles and trucks. In 1917 they were also awarded a contract to build recoil mechanisms for 155mm artillery pieces for France during World War I. John Dodge met with US Secretary of War Newton Baker and a delegation of French manufacturers to negotiate the deal. The French offered to send their skilled machinists to Detroit to teach Dodge how to build them. Secretary Baker commented that it would be a good idea.

John Dodge replied in his usual salty language." We don't need any Frenchmen to teach us anything. Just send us the damn blueprints."

Baker spoke up. "Look here, Mr. Dodge, I am not used to being spoken to in that kind of language."

"Maybe the war would be a whole lot better off if you were" blustered John. Somehow they still got the contract. They also supplied military cars, trucks and ambulance chassis during World War I. General Black Jack Pershing ordered his officers to use exclusively Dodge staff cars. This helped Dodge vehicles get a reputation for toughness and reliability.

Dodge continued to build their domestic car and truck business so that by 1920 they were second only to Ford in sales. Then tragedy struck. Both brothers died that year, John of influenza in January and Horace of cirrhosis of the liver in December. The Dodge Brothers had made a significant contribution to the development of the Ford Motor Company, one of the Big Three. Their own company, Dodge, was then managed by their widows. A few years later Dodge reemerged as a key part of another Big Three company, as we shall see.

Chapter 7. Billy Out at GM

In 1917 dramatic financial changes were affecting the automobile industry. America entered World War I, causing uncertainty in the stock market. GM's stock dropped from $200 to $75 a share. Billy, the eternal optimist, bought GM stock to shore up the price, figuring he would recover his losses when the market recovered. Unfortunately, he bought it "on margin", which meant he was essentially borrowing 90% of the value. When the stock dropped below his purchase price, his brokers "called" his stock and he didn't have the money to retain it. Board member Pierre Dupont became concerned with Billy's loss and bought large shares in GM to save the company. He clearly told Billy not to buy on margin again.

 Again in 1920 there was another recession and stocks dropped by 25%. Billy felt personally responsible for the stockholders whom he had convinced to invest, and he again began secretly buying stock on margin to shore up the value. As before, his margin purchases were called and he lost almost all of it. He had a fortune in excess of $90 million and six months later it was mostly gone.

Pierre du Pont called Billy in to his office. "Billy, you have made a mess of your investments again. There's no excuse for it a second time. If it becomes public that you lost so much, the publicity will be devastating for GM and weaken our stock. For this reason, we have decided to bail you out one last time. We are prepared to buy your remaining GM stock for $30 million, with one stipulation. You will resign completely from GM. I know you built this company yourself, and I wish there was another way, but there isn't. Unfortunately, you brought it on yourself."

Billy was quiet. Finally he said "I totally understand. I was sure this downturn was going to be a short one, and I would recover my money. Look, you are doing what you have to. Don't worry about me, I'll bounce back."

So one week short of his 59th birthday, he resigned from the company that he had single-handedly built. He never occupied an office in the Durant Building, which was completed 3 years after he left and renamed the General Motors Building. But bounce back he did. He founded Durant Motors within a month of leaving GM. Because his reputation had been protected by his GM buyout, he was able to raise $5 million by issuing stock in his new company. His first model, the Star, was followed by several other models. His plan was to have a line-up of models to compete with the various GM models.

Meanwhile GM continued to grow. Pierre du Pont headed up GM until 1923 when they promoted Alfred Sloan to President and then later to Chairman in 1937. Sloan professionalized the company by setting up formal organization charts with operating divisions and central staff functions. This decentralized management greatly reduced the number of executives reporting directly to him from the 70 some that had reported directly to Billy. Sloan's management structure became the model for corporations for years. He eventually grew GM into the world's largest corporation. Sloan was a highly talented organizer and builder, but without Billy Durant's entrepreneurial efforts there would have been nothing for him to organize and build!

Chapter 8. Walter Chrysler Gets His Own Company

After leaving GM, Walter Chrysler was hired as General Manager of a failing Willys-Overland Motor Company in Toledo, Ohio in 1919 at a salary of $1 million a year for two years. The banks holding loans to the company hired him to turn it around. After setting up his office there, he called in John Willys, one of the founders, who was President. "John, I'm cutting your salary from $150,00 a year to $75,000 a year. We need to cut costs."

"But surely there are other places to cut costs. I am President of the company, after all and have important responsibilities here and should be compensated for that."

"If you were worth $150,00 a year, I wouldn't be here. The investment bankers who hired me want new directions, and not whatever directions you were leading them. In fact, at $75,000 you are probably still overpaid."

Near the end of Walter's two-year contract, at a meeting to discuss renewing his salary, the bankers, though pleased with his progress in turning the company around, complained about his high salary. He replied, "If this is the way you feel, you can stick this job."

"Easy Walter, we were just negotiating. No need to get all up in arms about it."

"Well, you obviously don't appreciate what I have done for you, so I'm done here. I don't need this job."

Walter still had a passion for the automobile business, so he joined the Maxell Company, founded by Johnathan Maxwell and Ben Briscoe. At Willys, Walter had worked with 3 talented engineers, Fred Zeder, Owen Skelton and Carl Breer. Walter said of them "Those 3 young automotive engineers were wizards. You never would find, hunt high or low, three friends more harmoniously attuned, unless it might be those men of fiction, the Three Musketeers." And this is how they were referred to for many years. When Walter had left Willys, The Three Musketeers had also left and formed a consulting company. Walter hired them to design a new model for Maxwell. It was a 1924 Chrysler 6, and although it had a Chrysler nameplate it was still a Maxwell company model.

Walter personally exhibited the Chrysler 6 at the 1924 New York Auto Show. It did not qualify for admission to the show because it had not yet gone into production, so Walter arranged to display it in the lobby of the Commodore Hotel down the street. It was touted as quieter, smoother and quicker than anything in its price range of around $2000. The company said it gave the thrills of a $5000 car. The orders rolled in and soon Maxwell was one of three most profitable companies along with GM and Ford.

In June of 1925 a new company, the Chrysler Corporation was formed, and Maxwell was merged in. Their attorney, Nicholas Kelly was elected President. Walter could not be president because he was still President of Maxwell. The stockholders then dissolved Maxwell and transferred all its stock to Chrysler Corporation. So 18 days after the founding of Chrysler, Kelly stepped down and Walter became President. Walter told a friend" It's odd, but the first Chrysler car was not made by Chrysler Corporation and I was not its first President."

In 1926 Walter had lunch with an old associate from GM, KT Keller, who was now heading up GM of Canada. "Good to see you, KT. Looks like you are doing well at GM. I always knew you would, you are a hands-on guy like me. You really know your manufacturing."

"Thanks, Walter I always enjoyed working with you."

"Well, how would you like to work with me again? I need a Vice President of Manufacturing here at Chrysler. You are the best guy around, and I want nothing but the best. You have a nice spot at GM, I know, but only in one division, the Canadian operation. Here you would be involved in the whole company, running all our operations. How about it? Want to work together again? We can really grow Chrysler!"

"Walter, you intrigue me. GM is getting to be a huge company, and I could get lost there. But significant ground floor opportunity with your new company is tempting. Very tempting."

"Good," replied Walter as he leaned forward in his chair. "Now let's talk about money and work out a deal." And work out a deal they did. KT Keller joined Chrysler Corporation. And they grew Chrysler into a major competitor. They added the luxury Imperial line in 1927, the lower priced Plymouth line in 1928 and the DeSoto line shortly after.

Chrysler needed more plant capacity for the new models. Walter met with Clarence Read of the Dillon Read investment firm in a suite at the Ritz Hotel in New York. Dillon Read now owned the Dodge company which they had purchased from the widows of the Dodge Brothers. They wanted to sell Dodge to Walter. Walter complained, "You guys want way too much money for the company, Clarence."

Avoiding Walter's point, Clarence replied "It's a great company, with great product lines. It needs an automotive guy at the top, not us financial types."

"I have enough product lines, I just need more plant capacity to build them. That's all I need, and I don't want to pay for the product lines, just the plants."

"But you can have both, Walter. Keep the Dodge brand and also build your new Chrysler models and you will grow even faster."

"I'll take that into consideration. There is obviously additional value in buying the Dodge brand", Walter added firmly. "But even then your price is too damn high. I know you can come down some." And so it went, back and forth for 5 days holed up in the hotel. Finally they reached a deal, and Chrysler owned Dodge. KT Keller was promoted to head up the Dodge division, and the Chrysler Corporation had just taken a major step in growth.

Chapter 9. Changes at Ford

The Ford Motor Company had only one brand, Ford, which was known for its low cost and high quality. But things were about to change. On a cold day in February of 1922 Henry Ford and his son Edsel were driving to the office of Henry Leland, President of Lincoln Motor Car Company in Detroit. Lincoln was started back in 1917 by Leland and his son Wilford after he was fired from Cadillac by Billy Durant for not focusing enough on sales. Unfortunately for Leland, Lincoln was now in financial trouble. As Edsel drove, Henry spoke up. "I hope this Lincoln purchase works out as well as you think it will, Edsel. Eight million dollars is a lot of money for a failing company."

"I know, father, but we've needed a luxury car for a long time. This is our chance to get one without a lot of development costs and it's really a bargain at that price."

"Edsel, we really don't need a luxury car. I have often said that a Ford will carry you anywhere except into society. I know your wealthy friends in Grosse Pointe keep telling you that they want to buy a Ford automobile, but that a Model T is not fancy enough for them."

"And there are a lot of other people in the country who feel the same" replied Edsel." With our manufacturing knowledge and the Ford name, we can be very successful in the luxury car market."

"You know I will never put the Ford name on a luxury car. The name Ford means quality and economy and that is why we are successful."

"That's why this Lincoln deal is so good. We'll keep the Lincoln name for the car, but people will also know that they will get the Ford quality because we are making the cars."

"I hope you're right on this. This project is your baby, and you'll get the credit or the blame, depending on how it turns out."

"I'm confident that I can turn Lincoln around. Their styling is out of date for their market. I have some design ideas that will make a big impact."

"Well, here we are at Henry Leland's office. Let's go in, meet with him and his son and get the deal signed. Then you need to get cracking and get some payoff for our $8 million investment as soon as possible."

Lincoln went on to be a very successful brand for the Ford Motor Company, and Edsel Ford's pride and joy. Edsel added the Mercury brand in 1938 to be priced between the Ford and Lincoln brands. Mercury was a successful product line for many years but was discontinued in 2010.

In 1927 Edsel Ford spoke with Henry again about a very serious problem. "Father, Chevrolet is eating our lunch. We need to update the model T to compete with Chevy. People want hydraulic brakes, a 3-gear transmission, different colors, and they want more comfort. And Chevy is giving it to them at a price almost comparable to ours."

"Almost" replied Henry. "But we still have the lowest price. We brought our price down from $850 to $260 for basically the same car by using our moving assembly line. I have said in the past that there is one rule for the industrialist, and that is to make the best quality of goods possible at the lowest possible cost, paying the highest wages possible. We've been doing that ever since we came out with the $5.00 a day wage back in 1914. More people drive Fords than any other car. We have 50% of the market; that tells us we are right. Why change when we are winning?"

"Because Chevy is coming on strong and starting to overtake us. Everyone has started using an assembly line and bringing down their costs too. We can't wait for a new model until it is too late, or Chevy will be number one; we've almost waited too long already. This isn't the first time we have talked about this as you know. We've got this huge new Rouge plant almost ready, let's build a new model there. We have some great design ideas. It's a car you will be proud of."

"I know people call me stubborn behind my back, but I call it strength, not stubbornness. A lot of people have tried to change my mind over the years, and I had to be strong. Do you think we would be number one if I had given in every time someone wanted to change things? Do you think the Model T would be the top selling car for the last 15 years if I had kept changing things? Of course not. Call me stubborn if you want, but also call me successful. Sometimes I wish you had a little more of my stubbornness. You listen to too many people and let them influence you. I'm afraid that's what you are doing now."

"You just need to look at the sales figures, Father. You can see the Chevy is increasing each year and it's just a matter of time. And Walter Chrysler has just launched his company and he is no slouch. He will undoubtably be coming out with a lower price car to compete in our market too. Now is the time to make our move. I know you don't want to give up being number one."

"You really feel strongly about this, don't you? Of course we can't give up first place. If you really believe that will happen, I will take another look at the sales figures. It is tough to think of giving up the Model T. It's my baby, and it has made Ford a household name around the world."

"I understand. I know it'll be tough for you. But think of the new model as a new baby, one that will be even better known. With that Rouge plant, we can kick out new product at a great rate and hold our market lead."

"What would we call this new 'baby', Edsel?"

"I thought we could go back and honor your first model, the Model A."

"I like that. Kind of a sense of company history to it. The Ford Model A. And son, I also like your new streak of stubbornness, that you have stuck to your guns and fought me on this idea. I'm glad to see you more confident in yourself. As you've heard me say, if you think you can, or you think you can't, you are probably right. I am beginning to see that it might be time for a change. Let's give a real hard look at building this new Model A. If we do decide, I know it will be a real winner again." The

Highland Park Plant was shut down for 6 months in 1927 to retool and begin producing new Model A. Later, when the Rouge plant began full production it also built the Model A, which was a very successful car.

On October 21, 1929, a week before the stock market crash, Henry Ford organized the Light's Golden Jubilee to celebrate the 50th anniversary of his friend Thomas Edison's invention of the incandescent lamp. He also used that occasion to dedicate the Edison Institute of Technology at Greenfield Village in Dearborn. The celebrity guests included President Herbert Hoover, Orville Wright, Marie Curie, Will Rogers and of course automotive pioneers Billy Durant and Walter Chrysler. The three auto leaders chatted at the social hour before the dinner.

"Henry", commented Billy, "This is quite an event you have put together for Mr. Edison. He certainly deserves this recognition as one of history's greatest inventors."

"Right", added Walter, "He even outshines the three of us automotive inventors."

"By far," chimed in Henry. "I don't think we're even in the same boat with Edison."

"Don't sell us short, fellows," Billy exclaimed emphatically. "We invented the motorized age and changed the American way of life. Especially you, Henry, with your Model T, the car for the masses. The rest of us are just catching up with you. I don't know if my Durant Motors will catch you, but I am sure out to try!"

"As you know, GM has caught up with me," Henry complained." I know you are not a part of GM anymore, but it was your darned Chevrolet that did it. You know I'm not giving up my top spot without a fight."

Walter chimed in "You may do it with that new Model A of yours. It's a great competitor, Henry. But I haven't been just sitting on my ass watching this. Look out for my new Plymouth brand. This will be a great

3-way race between Ford, GM and Chrysler. And let's not forget you, Billy. I know you have great plans for your Durant Motors."

"I sure do. Look, you guys have the jump on me. You probably realize that it's harder to enter the market now than when we all started out. So it'll take me a little longer to get up steam, but let there be no doubt, I will be a contender for the top spot before long.

Walter spoke up. "So Henry, tell us a little more about this Edison Institute you are dedicating today."

"Well, it is a place where young people can live and study the sciences. A part of the Institute is my museum. For years I have been collecting historical items: automobiles, kitchen stoves, farm machinery, and a whole bunch of other items. So now I have a museum where I can keep them. I believe in practical education, the hands-on kind that the three of us had. The students in the institute can use my museum as a place to actually see and touch the history of science."

"That's great," said Walter." I wish I would have had a school like that to attend. My school was the school of life, and a few correspondence courses. What an opportunity for these young people!"

"There is one more part to this Institute, and that is the Greenfield Village I'm building. I started with Edison's laboratory from Menlo Park where he invented the electric lamp, and I'm adding dozens of other original buildings such as the Wright Brother's bicycle shop which I'm moving here from Dayton, Ohio. When these are completed, I plan to open it to the public so they can also enjoy this history."

"That's wonderful." stated Billy, smiling. "What a great place it'll make for families to bring their children to see and learn."

Henry interrupted "Well, fellows, I hate to break this off, but it is time to go to dinner. We don't want to keep our guest of honor, Tom Edison and our key speaker, President Hoover, waiting."

The Model A sold well and was an excellent product. But Henry's stubbornness had cost him the lead. The Chevrolet brand had jumped ahead of Ford in 1927, and for the first time since 1911 GM was the industry leader. Ford briefly jumped back ahead in 1930 on the back of the new Model A, but GM took over again in 1931 and stayed ahead of the Ford Motor Company for years based on the success of their Chevrolet brand plus their sales of the Buick, Oldsmobile, Pontiac, and Cadillac brands. Henry finally came out with his last major personal innovation in 1932 with his flathead V-8 engine which satisfied the consumer's desires for more power. The flathead V-8 was installed in several models which had specific model names, but mostly they were known as a Ford V-8.

Edsel went to Henry's office carrying a letter in his hand. "We got an interesting letter praising our new V-8. Does the name Clyde Barrow ring a bell?"

"No, it doesn't."

"Have you ever heard of Bonnie and Clyde?"

"Oh, those are the infamous bank robbers, right?"

"Right. Let me read you this letter.

> Mr. Henry Ford
> Detroit Mich
>
> Dear Sir:
>
> While I still I have got breath in my lungs I will tell you what a dandy car you make. I have drove Fords exclusively when I could get away with one. For sustained speed and freedom from trouble the Ford has got every other car skinned, and even if my business hasn't been strictly legal it don't hurt anything to tell you what a fine car you got in the V-8.
>
> Yours truly
> Clyde Champion Barrow.

What do you think of that, Father?"

"I know a lot of people are impressed with my V-8 engine, but that endorsement takes the cake!"

Chapter 10. Growth at GM

GM President Alfred Sloan had some outstanding talent to help him build the company. The inventor of the self-starter back in 1912, Charles Kettering, headed up the industry's first research and development department at GM. Kettering had the nickname "Boss", acquired years ago when he was the unofficial head of a group of engineers at National Cash Register who spent weekends in a barn experimenting with products for the newly emerging automobile industry and called themselves 'The Barn Gang.' They later formed Delco, whose purchase by GM brought in Kettering.

One day in 1934 Kettering came to see Sloan at his office. As he sat down across the desk from Sloan, he said, "Al, as you know, our diesel locomotive engines are gaining in popularity. I just saw some figures that show that Union Pacific has cut the travel time from the West Coast to Chicago from about 60 hours to about 40 hours using our engines and has reduced their operating costs per mile."

"Right,", commented Al." You should be real proud of those engines that your research group has developed."

"Al, the railroads are now asking if we could build an entire locomotive instead of just the engine."

Al paused briefly. "That would be quite an undertaking, what do you think?"

"I'd like to give it a try, and design an experimental locomotive."

"How much money would you need for the project?"

"About $500,000 is my estimate. I know that's a lot, but the payoff would be great if it works. There is a nice profit margin in locomotives."

"Boss, in my experience with new development projects of this scale, $500,000 probably is not enough!"

"I know", said Kettering, smiling, "but I figure if we spend that much you'll come through with the rest if you see we are on the right track." Sloan agreed to give him the money, and the Electo-Motive Division went on to be a major success in building diesel locomotives. GM also diversified further with the Frigidaire refrigerator division and North American Aviation.

In February of 1939, Kettering asked to meet with Alfred Sloan in his office. Al opened the conversation. "What's up, Boss?"

"We have an exciting new development to talk to you about. It's a transmission without a clutch."

"A what?" exclaimed Al." Did you say a transmission without a clutch? I know I'm not quite as technical as you, but I know you need a clutch to shift gears."

"Not anymore. We can use a fluid system to allow the transmission to change gears as the car speed increases. We call it the Hydra-matic. We would like you to drive a car with a prototype transmission installed."

"Certainly, I would have to see it to believe it. If it does work, it sounds pretty pricey. Sounds like it will kick up the price of the car."

"To be honest, it will. But think of the marketing appeal. Particularly to women drivers. More and more women are driving, and many get frustrated with shifting the gears. Also it is better in slow traffic, you don't have to keep up-shifting and down-shifting all the time. We think that with these advantages many customers would be willing to pay the extra cost. We can offer it as an option to the standard transmission so they will have a choice. We were thinking it might be best to offer it first on the Cadillac, because the base price is higher, and the extra cost would be a smaller percentage."

Al leaned forward in his chair." Well, even if this thing works as you say, I would not want to try it on our top brand." Chuckling, he added. "As you

48

know, the word Cadillac has come to mean the best in the industry. I even heard of one toilet company that says that their toilet is the 'Cadillac of the Industry'. We can't take a chance on messing up our Cadillac image with a possible problem transmission. No, let's consider using it on the Oldsmobile. Still a high base price, but not a risk to our top brand."

"Fine with me "replied Kettering." I don't care about which car we use, I just want to get it out in the market to prove itself. And I am convinced it will."

Al took his ride in the prototype and was impressed. The Hydra-matic transmission was first offered on the 1940 Oldsmobile and was an astounding success, paving the way for automatic transmissions to eventually be the preferred option by most customers. It was eventually offered on all GM models and it was also sold to other car manufacturers until they developed their own designs.

One day in 1940 Alfred Sloan called his marketing Vice President, Patrick Calhoun into his office. "Pat, I want to bounce an idea off you. We have several very successful models, but sometimes they compete with each other. I'd like to organize our pricing structure a little more formally. Let's cut down on the price overlap, so that customers can see a more clear difference between the models. Chevy is our base model, and then Pontiac will be the next step. More features, higher price. The next step is Olds, then Buick, more luxury. The final step is Cadillac, the most luxurious and the most expensive. Then people can see clearly which model their income will allow them to buy."

"I get it. Then as their income increases, they'll want to move up the line. Brilliant!"

"'You got it. That's the plan."

"Let me run one of my ideas by you, now, Al. How about if we introduce small changes every year so that even if they are not ready to move up,

49

they'll want to trade in their car for this year's new model of their current brand? We can even make a big deal out of the new model introductions each fall to whet their interest. This can produce significantly greater annual sales."

Al's eyes lit up. "I like that. I like that a lot! I think with these two ideas we'll have a marketing approach that will keep us well ahead of our competition. Of course, I bet they will catch on to what we're doing and copy us. But only after it has given us the jump on the market. Let's do it!" The GM brand differentiation and annual changes were very profitable for GM and were eventually copied by several other manufacturers.

Chapter 11. Chrysler Becomes a Major Competitor

Chrysler added a luxury brand in 1927, the Imperial L-80, with a top speed of 80 mph. They then added the lower priced Plymouth brand in 1928 to compete with Ford and Chevrolet. Plymouth featured Floating Power engine mounts which reduced vibration and made the ride much smoother, which was a strong competitive advantage. They next added the DeSoto brand to fit the market between their Plymouth and Chrysler brands. In 1928 Walter Chrysler was named Time Magazine's Man of the Year for his accomplishments in building this major company in just 3 years.

That same year Walter financed the construction of the Chrysler Building in New York City. It was built with his own funds and was not a Chrysler Corporation project. He told a reporter "I was well aware that a rich man's sons are likely to be cheated out of something. How could my boys ever know the wild incentive that burned in me from the time I first watched my father put his hand to the throttle of his engine? I could not give them that, but it was through this thinking that I conceived of putting up a building that could be theirs to manage." When completed in 1930 it was the tallest building in the world, surpassing even the Eiffel Tower in Paris. It kept that title for 11 months, until the Empire State Building was completed in 1931.

The Plymouth brand proved to be a life-changer for Chrysler. It continued to grow and by 1932 it was third in sales behind Chevrolet and Ford. By the end of 1932 GM, Ford and Chrysler produced 85% of the total output of American cars, and the term The Big Three was born. In January, 1934, a special issue of Fortune Magazine was devoted to Walter Chrysler and his success with building his company. That month, Billy Durant hosted a lunch for the Big Three auto pioneers in a small private dining room at the Pontchartrain Hotel during the Detroit auto show, to honor Walter.

Billy Durant opened the discussion. "Fellows, I'm glad we could all get together. I thought it would be a good idea to honor Walter. After all, it's not everyone that gets a special edition of Fortune magazine. Besides, I heard that he is thinking of retiring next year, so this may be kind of a 'last supper' for the founders of the Big Three. I hope no one gets crucified as a result, though." The other two chuckled. "Just remember, Walter, that I brought you into the auto business when I was running GM."

"Yes, and I imagine you remember why I left," Walter said smiling.

"I know I wasn't the easiest guy to work for. You did a great job running Buick, and you know I hated to lose you."

"I know you had a hard time letting go of some things, Billy, but it worked out well. I learned a lot at Buick. Enough to start my own company eventually. I certainly appreciate my time there. Yes, I'll probably retire next year. I still will be Chairman, but I won't be involved in active management. I'm leaving that to KT Keller."

"Henry, we know that you've turned the Ford presidency over to Edsel some time ago," commented Billy." But I hear you are still pretty active in management."

"Yes, I still have a lot of say in the company. Some feel that I have too much say, but I still have plenty of good ideas and I don't want to waste them. Also, between the three of us here, Edsel sometimes gets off on the wrong track and I need to steer him back."

"Well," interjected Walter," I'm leaving all the steering to KT once I leave. I have a nice home in New York, on the water on Long Island with a great view of the Sound. I have a nice boat and am looking forward to enjoying life. I have earned it. Billy, are you ever going to retire? You are older than me. When are you going to relax and enjoy life?"

Billy leaned back in his chair. "As you probably know, I lost interest in my car company and got more interested in investments. I started some stock pools where people could invest more easily. One of my partners was Joe Kennedy. You might have heard that they called me 'King of the Bulls' on Wall Street back then. That is, until the market crash back in 29. Almost wiped me out financially. During this time Durant Motors fell on hard times and we had to declare company bankruptcy last year. But to answer your question about retirement, I am more like Henry. I guess work is my answer to enjoying life. I may never retire. I have a new venture that I am excited about. Bowling alleys."

"Bowling alleys?" questioned Henry.

"Right," replied Billy, his eyes lighting up." Now you only find them in fancy hotels, private clubs and office buildings. I think there is a market for public bowling alleys where anyone can go, pay a fee and bowl with friends and family. And have a drink and some lunch, too."

"Sounds interesting, "commented Walter." Is there enough money in that for someone like you? You are used to big-time operations."

"There certainly is. I'm planning the first one in Pontiac, and once that is going, I envision a national company. I'm shooting for about 50 alleys in the first three years."

Henry jumped in, "Billy, if it was anyone but you, I would not give it a rat's chance of success. But you seem to be able to sell anything. Why not bowling alleys? Besides, we won't have you competing with us anymore," he added with a wry smile. "Best of luck to you in your venture."

"Thanks, Henry. Now we should be winding up our meal here. Back to the main purpose of getting together. I propose a toast to Walter. We know you have several months left before you go, but we are happy we could get together and wish you a happy retirement. So here is the best to you in the future," he said lifting his wine glass.

"Cheers," added Henry, raising his glass of lemonade. "The very best to you."

A couple months later, before he retired, Walter called K.T. Keller into his office. "I want you to look at this idea I have for a new model. Just look at it. What do you think?"

"Well, it certainly is different", K.T. replied somewhat skeptically. "Not quite like anything I have ever seen."

"That's the idea. It's called streamlining. The railroads are doing it with their new locomotives, and the aircraft industry is also doing it. It cuts down on the air resistance and cuts fuel costs. I plan on calling it the Airflow. I'm really excited about it."

"It does make sense. I just wonder if it is too radical in appearance for most customers."

"That's where we have to sell it. Show them that their new car will be way ahead of their neighbor's in looks and performance. Just think how this will look in magazine ads!"

"Walter, you have always had a good eye for design. I say go for it!"

Go for it they did, but go for it the customers did not. It was too different. Auto design is a tough business. You have to be out ahead of the competition, but not too far ahead, and they were. After the Airflow was on the market a few months, sales were dismal. Walter called K.T. in again. "K.T., what are we going to do? We are losing our ass on this Airflow. I guess it's too much of a change for most customers. Maybe they will start to accept it, but we can't afford to wait."

"I've been thinking about this. You know, we could keep the basic running gears of the car and put a more conventional body on it. Keep a bit of the streamlining, but get rid of the drastic look. Also make it a new model, get rid of the Airflow name.

"Ok, do it. I hope it works. I'll trust you that you'll make it work. But let's use a name that still focuses on the streamlining idea, though. I think that still has some good sales value. How about Airstream?"

"Fine, as long as we identify it as a different model. I'll get right on it."
The Airstream was introduced in 1935 and outsold the Airflow 5-1, putting the Airstream in the black.

Walter retired as President later in 1935 and thoroughly enjoyed his home on Long Island Sound. He remained as Chairman and CEO but was rarely involved in management. He had 4 children, 2 sons and 2 daughters, none of whom were involved in the automotive industry. His son Walter Jr. founded the Chrysler Museum in Norfolk, Virginia which was not an automotive museum, but rather an art museum.

Chapter 12. The Workers Get a Voice in the Big Three

Automotive workers were beginning to form unions like employees had in other industries such as the garment and mining industries. In February of 1937 Alfred Sloan, Chairman of GM, met with Michigan Governor Frank Murphy at Sloan's office. After a handshake, Sloan opened the conversation. "As I told you, Frank, I won't meet with John L. Lewis on this strike at our Fisher Body plant in Flint. In the first place, Lewis is from the mining industry, not the auto industry. I know he is President of the Congress of Industrial Organizations, so I guess that's why the United Auto Workers called him in to negotiate. As a new union without any successes yet, they called in a big gun to negotiate for them. Second, this is not the usual strike where the organizers form picket lines outside to keep workers from coming into work. This is a sit-down strike. They're staying in the plant, sitting down on the job, so we can't bring in scab workers to replace them. If I met with Lewis, I would be acknowledging the United Auto Workers, and I would be allowing this kind of sit-down strike which could start a dangerous precedent for us and other auto companies. Since the strike has gone on for a month now, I agreed to have you negotiate as a mediator, but not representing us officially. This strike is costing GM big bucks, and is hurting the economy of Flint and Michigan."

"That's why I'm here," replied Frank grimly. "We have got to find a way to stop this thing. It's hurting us all. Now, the union wants a 10% pay increase, which seems reasonable to me based on the hard work they do to keep up with the assembly line and production schedules. The union leaders also want to be allowed to talk to workers about the union on their unpaid lunch breaks. Again, that seems like a freedom of speech issue to me, and hard to stop on a legal basis. And they want a closed shop, where if the union is voted in, every worker must join and pay dues. Otherwise some are getting the union benefits without paying their share."

"I've talked with my GM Board, and here is where we are. We could do a 5% pay raise, but not 10%. We are ok with allowing the workers the freedom to talk at lunch about the union. But we will never, I repeat never, have a closed shop. Those workers who want to join the union will pay their dues, but they cannot force all workers to join and pay dues. Workers should have that freedom of choice. If you think you can sell that deal to John L Lewis, we have a deal." Frank Murphy did sell John L Lewis on the deal, and Lewis got the UAW to accept it and the strike was settled after 44 days. The UAW was officially recognized by one of the Big Three for the first time.

This inspired the workers at Chrysler to initiate their own sit-down strike. In March, they struck all six Chrysler plants in Detroit. Governor Murphy again tried to be the mediator, but this time the UAW wanted to negotiate directly with Chrysler Management. So Walter Chrysler, even though he had retired as President, was still CEO, and agreed to negotiate with John L. Lewis who was again negotiating for the UAW.

Walter stretched out his hand to Lewis. "John, let's settle this thing quickly. Chrysler cannot afford a 44- day strike like GM had, especially since they're striking all our plants. The workers can't afford to be without pay that long either. What do your guys want?"

"They want the same contract as GM, Walter, but they also want a closed shop. They were real disappointed that they did'nt get that at GM. It doesn't set well with the workers that support the union and get everyone's pay raised, when they see some workers not joining and not paying dues."

"Well, that's tough, but it's not Chrysler's problem", commented Walter rather sternly. "The UAW needs to sell the benefits of union membership to them, not force them to join and pay dues. This is a free county. People are free to work for Chrysler and they are free to leave. We try to take care of our employees so that they don't want to leave. The union will have to do the same thing. You are going to have to go back and tell that to the UAW leadership. If they insist on a closed shop, they will not be recognized as a bargaining unit for employees at Chrysler. Hell, they didn't get their closed shop at GM and they are not getting it at Chrysler. I said we can't afford a long strike here, but we'll hold out as long as we have to on that issue even though it would cost us dearly. It would hurt us as a company, and would hurt the workers too. Sales will be lost for us, and jobs will be lost for workers. You tell them that." Lewis told them, they listened, and they settled without a closed shop. Their strike lasted 29 days, compared to 44 days for the GM strike. John L. Lewis praised Walter Chrysler as a man of his word.

In May of that same year the UAW tried to organize Ford. Union organizers were attempting to hand out fliers at shift change on the pedestrian overpass over Miller Road at the Ford Rouge Plant. A Detroit News photographer asked Walter Reuther and several other union leaders to pose for a photograph with the Ford sign in the background. Suddenly men from Ford's Service Department, an internal security force, attacked and beat Reuther and several other leaders. The beatings were captured by the photographer and his photos and story, known as the Battle of the Overpass, made headlines in newspapers across the country. The head of the Ford Service Department, ex-boxer Harry Bennet, was chastised by the National Labor Relations Board, which hurt Ford's reputation across the country. Ford already had a tainted reputation in employee relations due to an episode back in 1932 during the depression, when thousands of people marched on the Rouge Plant to protest a 50% reduction in wages which did not allow them to feed their families. Ford security guards and Dearborn police fired on the crowd killing 5 protesters. This event became known as the Ford Hunger March.

In 1941 Harry Bennet fired 8 employees for union organizing which sparked a massive sit-down strike. After 10 days Henry Ford's wife Clara had had enough of violence and talked to Henry one evening after dinner. "Henry, I am tired of violence between our company and our workers. I'm fearful that there will be more violence during this strike. If you keep this up, what kind of a company will you leave for our children to run? I don't want them to always be on the side of force every time our workers have an issue. GM and Chrysler have learned that it's better to let the employees have a group to negotiate for them and it's working fine for them."

"Clara, we treat our workers fairly. We were the first to double their pay back in 1914 with the $5.00 a day wage and we reduced the workday from 9 hours to 8 hours. Our people like to work for Ford and they don't need any outsiders to help them deal with us."

"I know you led the way in improving things for your workers, dear, but things have changed since we grew so big. Our workers don't know you personally anymore, and you have Harry Bennet dealing with the employees. I never liked him, and neither does Edsel."

"Harry does a good job for us. He makes sure our production figures are good, and yes he does get rid of the slackers."

"Henry, I can't take this violence anymore. Go ahead and keep the union out, and you may find that I am out too!" And with that she rose, slammed the door and stalked out! "Henry did some soul searching and settled with the UAW. Ironically, the Ford contract finally gave the union a closed shop for the first time. Harry Bennet was fired by Henry Ford II when he eventually took over company management from his grandfather.

Chapter 13. The Arsenal of Democracy

By December 1940 Germany had invaded France and much of the rest of
Europe. Americans had had enough of war during WWI, and there was
little interest in getting involved in another overseas conflict where
Americans would die defending other countries. But President Franklin
Delano Roosevelt had a longer view and felt that we must support our
allies England and Russia. He thought if they fell, eventually America
would also be invaded. So on December 29 he addressed the country on
the radio in one of his famous Fireside Chats.

"The people of Europe who are defending themselves do not ask us to do
their fighting. They ask us for the implements of war, the planes, the
tanks, the guns, the freighters which will enable them to fight for their
liberty and for our security. Emphatically we must get these weapons to
them, get them to them in sufficient volume and quickly enough, so that
we and our children will be saved the agony and suffering of war which
others have had to endure. We must be the great "arsenal of
democracy." Within weeks Congress passed the Lend-Lease bill so that
we could lend armaments to our allies without us being directly involved
in the war.

FDR asked GM President Bill Knudsen to resign from GM and head up all
defense production for the nation, and he did. Knudsen, a tall, lanky
individual of Danish birth, set up a meeting with the leaders of the Big
Three early in 1941. This included Edsel Ford, GM CEO Alfred Sloan, and
Chrysler President KT Keller. "Welcome to this meeting, gentlemen. As
you know, we have a monumental task ahead of us. FDR has asked me to
head up this venture to supply military equipment to our allies, in huge
volumes and at rapid speed. You have all received the letter I sent you
asking you each to come prepared today to tell us what you can

contribute. So let's get right to it. Who would like to start?"

Edsel Ford spoke up "My father and I have discussed this, and here are our thoughts. Consolidated Aircraft in San Diego has a bomber, the B-24, that they have started producing. They don't have the production capacity to make enough of them, and we've been asked to make parts for them in our auto plants. We're going down shortly to meet with them on that project. Also, the Bantam Company in California has a small vehicle they call a General Purpose vehicle, nicknamed the GP. When they talk about it, it sounds like they are saying Jeep. Willys has agreed to make about half of what is needed, and we will make the other half amounting to about 600,000 units. Those are our major contributions planned to date, but I'm sure we will take on more." He paused briefly. "Let me just add one thing. As you all know, my father has been a strong pacifist, but when FDR called father agreed to back him completely on this program."

"Thanks, and say Hi to Henry from us all. Who wants to go next?"

Alfred Sloan interjected." Bill, we are going to miss you at GM, but we all agree that this is the most important use of your abilities right now. Charlie Wilson has stepped up as President to replace you at GM and will do a fine job. Our major product will be military trucks. Our GMC Division is readily equipped to modify some of our present vehicles and add others as needed. They already have an idea for a brand-new amphibious vehicle. They call it the Duck. I can't wait to ride in the protype. You may see me cruising around in the Detroit River in one soon. We're also looking into some aircraft and aircraft engine products."

" That sounds great," commented Bill. "I want a ride in the Duck vehicle, too. Not for fun, mind you," he smiled, "but to evaluate it in my role overseeing military production."

KT Keller spoke up" I guess I'm up now, Bill. We have committed to an aggressive program of building tanks. Rather than try to convert our auto plants, we are building a new plant in Warren Township. Nothing there now but cornfields, but very soon you will see the Detroit Arsenal Tank

Plant there. We are committing to build 1000 tanks there by August of next year."

"That is a real tight schedule", replied Bill. "A brand-new plant and 1000 tanks, all in a year and a half. Good luck and I hope you can pull it off. Well, it looks like we are all set for today. Everyone keep me posted of your progress, and I'll also be following up with each of you. You are all a key to helping our allies defend their countries and keep the threats from reaching our shores."

Edsel and his production manager Charlie Sorenson made a trip to San Diego and were staying at the Del Coronado hotel. They toured the Consolidated Aircraft plant and saw how they were building B-24 bombers at stationary locations. The next day they met with John Bullington, the Consolidated production manager in a conference room off the plant floor. "John, thank you for the tour yesterday", said Edsel. "We see a problem here. You will never be able to meet the production schedule with this approach, even if we make parts for you. The final assembly step will be a bottleneck. Now there is another approach, and that's to use an assembly line."

Bullington chuckled and said, "This is the aircraft industry, not the auto industry, Edsel. You may be able to build cars on an assembly line, but you could never meet our quality standards that way. If something goes wrong with a plane, you can't just pull it off on the shoulder the way you can with a car. Peoples' lives depend on our quality. It is something you cannot rush, and your assembly line would do that."

Edsel retorted, a bit irritated. "We can control the speed of an assembly line, and of course a B-24 line would move much slower than an auto assembly line. But we know how to build quality and are confident we can do it."

Bullington asked "Even if you could do that, how big of a plant would you need to build aircraft? It would have to be huge."

"Charlie, show him your idea," chimed in Edsel.

Charlie pulled out a piece of hotel stationary. "I was playing around with this last night after our tour. This is a rough sketch of a plant that would do the job. Here are the sub-assembly areas, feeding into the final assembly line."

"My god," said Bullington." That would be one helluva long plant! Do you have a plant like that to convert?"

"No "answered Charlie." We would have to build one, but we have the land in the Willow Run area near Dearborn."

"The war will be over by the time you can build that," said Bullington with a frown.

"We have an architect by the name of Albert Kahn who builds our plants" said Edsel confidently. "He can get it done in time. With this plant we estimate we can turn out one plane an hour, instead of one plane a week like this plant does."

"Holy shit," Bullington exclaimed. "One plane an hour. You've got to be kidding. Not in the aircraft business. No way! Look, fellows, you came down here to work out a deal to supply us parts. Now you're talking about building the whole plane. That was not the plan. And you have this crazy idea that you can build one bomber an hour. This has become laughable."

Edsel spoke up firmly. "The more I think about this, there is no way that with us only building parts for you that we can put enough B-24 bombers in the air to knock out Germany. We'll go back and present our ideas to Bill Knudsen and let him decide. I know a new plant will be costly, but so will losing the war. I'll have to clear it with my father, but I think Ford can donate the land for the plant. That will help cut the costs. I think we have what we need from this meeting, so thank you for your hospitality and we need to be on our way."

The Willow Run plant was built on land donated by Ford, and it produced over 9000 B-24 bombers, half the nation's output of that plane. And yes, they turned out one bomber per hour! The B-24 Liberator was considered the workhorse bomber of the war and contributed heavily to the defeat of Germany. FDR had urged America to be the Arsenal of Democracy, but that term became associated with the Detroit area because this region, and notably the Big Three auto companies, contributed over one third of the entire nation's military equipment.

Chapter 14. The Big Three Pioneers Exit the Scene

Walter Chrysler had a stroke at age 63 and died 2 years later in 1940. Chrysler was known as a motivator, and someone said of him that he built with men, not with companies or machines. It was also said of him that he had a glittering personality with a rich railroad man's vocabulary, a short temper and a showman's pride. His company continued as a major US corporation until 1998, when it was purchased by the German company Daimler-Benz. Technically this ended the Big Three as American auto makers, even though Chrysler has continued to be a major manufacturer in the US. After several mergers, it eventually ended up as a division of Stellantis, whose headquarters is in the Netherlands.

Edsel Ford, who had served as President of Ford since 1919 sadly died in 1943 from stomach cancer preceded by ulcers, which many people thought were brought on partly by the pressure from Henry constantly undercutting his decisions. Ford Motor Company had continued to grow, with a Ford dealer in almost every town in the US. Ford was also growing into an international power with plants in Canada, Europe, Latin America, Asia, South Africa and Australia.

Edsel's widow Eleanor met with Henry. "Henry, we need to promote someone to replace Edsel. There are several good candidates within company management. I think we should set up a committee of the Board to select one."

"Eleanor, we don't need to do that. I can run the company myself. I have been very closely involved while Edsel was President. I can pick right up where he left off. We won't miss a beat."

"I know you've been closely involved, too closely some people feel, but that is another issue. You are 78 and not in the best of health. This company is a major international company, much larger than when you were last President in 1919. We need someone that is up on all the new technology and is looking to the future to keep ahead of the competition."

"I can't think of anyone in our management that fits all that, Eleanor, and I don't want to go outside the company. We have always had a Ford in charge. I was hoping that one of my grandsons would be ready when Edsel stepped down. But they are all too young. Henry II will probably be the most capable when he is old enough. So I'll stay on until he is ready. Period."

"Henry," Eleanor stated strongly, "that just won't work in my book. I am sorry, but we have to accept the fact that you are not the one to run this big company. As one of the owners of the company, I can't let that happen for the sake of the company and the future of my four children. I was hoping I could convince you but evidently I can't."

"So who are you proposing to run it if I did step down?"

"My son Henry II is the most capable, as you've said. So he would be my choice."

"You have got to be kidding. He is only 26. Also, he's in the Navy. He is not available."

"We can get him out of the service because we are a military supplier and have a critical need for him. Tell you what. Let's get him out of the service and bring him in for a couple of years to learn as much as he can. That way we are not putting him in a sink or swim situation right away. Once we get finished with our wartime production of planes and weapons, he'll be ready to lead us back into commercial production again."

Henry leaned back in his chair and replied without much enthusiasm "Well, I guess there is no harm in getting one of my grandson's some company experience."

Two years later they met again. "It's time to step down now, Henry. My son can take over."

"He's not ready yet. I need to run the company for a while until he is ready."

"I'm sorry, but you are not up to the job anymore. Charlie Sorenson has really been running the war production, and Harry Bennett has been handling other management responsibilities. Charlie wants to retire, and you know what I think of Bennett. He is the last person I want running the company. We need a leader for the company, and the only one that makes sense is my son Henry II. So here is my position. If you don't step down, I'll sell my share of the company on the open market, and you will have outside stockholders. I know you said that you would never let that happen. But it will happen unless you step down. Then with outside directors on the board, they might appoint anyone president, and it most probably would not be a Ford."

Henry sat silently. Finally he said "You give me no real choice. If this is the only way to keep our company private, and have it run by a Ford, I will agree. It looks like you win, Eleanor."

"No, we all win. And the Ford Motor Company wins."

Henry did step down at age 80. The company had been in financial trouble before the war, and had been third behind Chevrolet and Chrysler in their markets. Henry Ford II, often referred to as Hank the Duce, moved into the presidency in 1945 at age 28 and turned the company around with the help of former GM executive Ernest Breech and a group of ten former military planners who became known as the Whiz Kids. They included Robert McNamara, who later became Secretary of Defense and then President of the World Bank. Eleanor was right. The change was needed, and her son Henry II was the right choice to provide it.

Henry Ford died in 1947 at age 83. Thousands of people paid their respects at his funeral at his beloved museum in Dearborn. Henry's Ford stock went to the Ford Foundation, making it the world's richest private foundation at the time. Because he was the first to capture the major share of the new automobile market, Henry Ford is known world-wide as the icon of the automobile industry. The Ford Motor Company in 2021 is still headed by a Ford, Henry's great-grandson William (Bill) Clay Ford, Jr.

Billy Durant hung on financially for 3 years after his Durant Motors went bankrupt, finally declaring personal bankruptcy in 1936. He opened his first bowling alley in Flint in 1940 but suffered a stroke in 1942 at age 80 and could not continue his dream of a national chain. He and his wife Catherine moved back to New York and were supported financially by four of his earlier colleagues: Alfred Sloan of GM, GM supplier C.S. Mott, President of GM of Canada Sam McLaughlin and John Thomas Smith, Billy's lawyer. Each month one of the four sent a check for $2500 to Catherine. Billy died at age 85 in 1947, the same year that Henry Ford passed away. In 1958 a marble slab monument was laid by the City of Flint in front of the Flint Cultural Center, inscribed with the following:

> "William Crapo Durant, 1861-1947, Founder of General Motors, 1908. In the golden milestone year of the corporation its proud birthplace dedicates this plaza in lasting appreciation of what his vision, genius and courage contributed to his home city and to the renown of American Industry."

So what is the final story on the Big Three? International competitors such as Toyota, Honda, Volkswagen and others increased their market share by building plants in the US, some surpassing the original Big Three in sales. So now GM, Ford and Chrysler are referred to as the Detroit Three rather than the Big Three. But Detroit still is and always will be referred to as the Motor City, due to the accomplishments of the original pioneers who founded the Big Three: Henry Ford the tinkerer, Billy Durant the salesman, and Walter Chrysler the motivator.

Appendix A. Individuals & Companies in the Formation of the Big Three

FORD

Detroit Automobile Company

Henry Ford

Henry Ford Company

Henry Ford

Ford Motor Company

Henry Ford
Edsel Ford
Henry Ford II

Lincoln Division

Henry Leland
Edsel Ford

GENERAL MOTORS

Buick Division

David Buick
Billy Durant
Charles Nash
Walter Chrysler

Oldsmobile Division

Ransom Olds
Fred Smith

Cadillac Division

Henry Leland

Oakland/Pontiac Division

Edward Murphy

Chevrolet Division

Billy Durant
Louis Chevrolet

United Motors

Billy Durant
Alfred Sloan

CHRYSLER

Chrysler Corporation
Walter Chrysler
 K.T. Keller

Dodge Division

John Dodge
Horace Dodge
K.T. Keller

Appendix B. Brief Biographies of the Big Three Pioneers

Louis-Joseph Chevrolet
   Born:1878
   Spouse: Suzanne Treyvoux
   Children: Charles Louis, Alfred Joseph Etienne
   Key Positions: Race Driver, Buick Division, General Motors
                  Co-founder, Chevrolet Motor Company
   Died: 1941

Walter Percy Chrysler
   Born: 1875
   Spouse: Della Viola Forker
   Children: Thelma Irene, Bernice, Walter Jr., Jack
   Key Positions: Works Manager, American Locomotive
                  Works Manager, Buick Division
                  President, Buick Division
                  General Manager, Willys-Overland
                  President, Maxwell Company
                  President, Chrysler Corporation
                  CEO, Chrysler Corporation
   Died: 1940

Horace Elgin Dodge
   Born:1868
   Spouse: Anna Thompson
   Children: Delphine, Horace Jr.
   Key Positions: Co-founder, Dodge Brothers Company
   Died: 1920

John Francis Dodge
   Born:1864
   Spouse(s): Ivy Hawkins, Isabelle Smith, Matilda Rausch
   Children: Anna Margaret, Winifred, Isabel, John Duval,
               Francis, Daniel
   Key Positions: Co-founder, Dodge Brothers Company
   Died: 1920

William (Billy) Crapo Durant
  Born: 1861
  Spouse(s): Clara Pitt, Catherine Lederer
  Children: Margery Pitt, Russell Clifford
  Key Positions: Co-founder, Durant- Dort Carriage Company
                 Founder: General Motors
                 Co-founder, Chevrolet Motor Company
  Died: 1947

Edsel Bryant Ford
  Born: 1893
  Spouse: Eleanor Clay
  Children: Henry II, William Clay Sr., Josephine Clay, Benson
  Key Positions: President, Ford Motor Company
  Died: 1943

Henry Ford
  Born: 1863
  Spouse: Clara Bryant
  Children: Edsel Bryant
  Key Positions: Engineer, Detroit Automobile Company
                 Vice President, Henry Ford Company
                 Founder, Ford Motor Company
  Died: 1947

Henry Martyn Leland
  Born: 1843
  Spouse: Ellen Rhonda Hull
  Children: Martha Gertrude, Wilfred Chester, Miriam Edith
  Key Positions: Founder, Cadillac Motor Company
                 Founder, Lincoln Motor Company
  Died: 1932

Charles Williams Nash

Born: 1864
Spouse: Jessie Halleck
Children: Mae, Lena
Key Positions: Vice President, Durant-Dort Carriage Co.
President, Buick Motor Company
President, General Motors Corporation
President, Nash Motors
Died:1948

Ransom Eli Olds
Born:1864
Spouse: Metta Ursula Woodward
Children: Bernice Estelle, Ralph Eli, Gladys Marguerite
Mildred
Key Positions: Founder, Olds Motor Vehicle Company
Founder, REO Motor Car Company
Died:1950

Alfred Pritchard Sloan Jr.
Born: 1875
Spouse: Irene Jackson
Key Positions: President, Hyatt Roller Bearing Company
President, United Motors Company
President, General Motors Corporation
Chairman, General Motors Corporation
Died: 1966

About the Author

Russell Lee Doré is a Board Member of the Motor Cities National Heritage Area, a former Board Member of the Henry Ford Heritage Association, and a member of the Northville Historical Society. His company, Doré Productions, has developed automotive history presentations which have been given to dozens of groups throughout the country. He holds bachelors, masters, and doctoral degrees in the social sciences, and has held management and employee development positions in the transportation industry and in consulting firms.

He lives with his wife Judy in Northville, Michigan in the Greater Detroit area. See *doreproductions.weebly.com* for information about his presentations.

Made in the USA
Monee, IL
05 June 2021